# THE SQUIRREL BOOK

*By the Same Author*
HEDGE FOLK IN TWILIGHT
SWIFT MOVEMENT IN THE TREES
WIDOW HEDGEHOG
LITTLE ANIMAL CLUB
A HOUSE IN THE WOODS
THE ARK

NUFFLES.

# THE SQUIRREL BOOK

*by*
*Phyllis Kelway*

*Illustrations by NEWTON WHITTAKER*

*Photographs by the Author*

**COLLINS**
**LONDON & GLASGOW**

*Copyright 1944*

PRINTED AND MADE IN GREAT BRITAIN
BY WM. COLLINS SONS AND CO. LTD.
LONDON AND GLASGOW

To

P E T E R

The Flight-Lieutenant

*In Memory of*

F O R T N U M

The Flying Squirrel

# ILLUSTRATIONS

# CHAPTER ONE

AFTER a ten-mile ride I leaned my bicycle against a stone wall and sat beside a stream. The sunlight was mirrored in the surface of the water so that I could not see deep down to where the fishes were. I moved to the flat shelf upstream, where the surface was dark and clear. The one called Blackout (because she had been born just then) flopped beside me, panting, with her red tongue out. Fixing her honest amber eyes upon me, she said it was dreadfully hot, and should she go for a swim? I said, no, not yet, because I thought sticklebacks might be in this stream, and she would stir up the mud with her paws. We shared the billy-can of tea together, and when we were less thirsty we were cooler too.

A moorhen jerked his way out from the bed of reed opposite, coughed apologetically when he saw us, and vanished into the forest stems. Blackout turned her face to me inquiringly. It was a long lean face, clean-cut, high-bred, and the eyes knew not only what happened now but what had happened before. Her black ears were pricked forward; she was asking questions; but we did not speak aloud, for in looking at her I called home her thoughts as she called mine. So we found an easy ledge of stone on which to lie, and I leaned over the water while she, with her eyes half-closed against the glare, watched the dragon flies swooping in violent bursts of speed from one bank to the other.

Far down in the water (yet only twelve inches below the surface) I could see the teeming life of the stream-bottom. The mud was never still; the weeds stirred and leaned downstream, and everywhere a shoal of tiny fishes flitted through the water like a flock of swallows through the air. Hundreds of sticklebacks, like miniature mackerel, drifted in formation before my eyes; but when my shadow fell upon them, they were gone.

Only one fish was left and that was a Robin stickleback, his belly crimson, his back glowing green and blue; and this one had stood valiantly at his post, while those other mobile sticklebacks without home ties fled for undisturbed waters. The Robin fanned his nest in the mud with his fins; he attacked a caddis-worm who had no other wish than to crawl from one stone to another, and he spat mud from his mouth, looking very fierce as he spat. Suddenly I felt the hunting instinct coming over me. I wanted stickle-backs at home to watch their spitting and their fierce glances, their fights and their ravenous feeding; and I knew that I must capture a few to take home to our stream. The Robin, brave fish, should stay at his post, but a dozen of the shoal, born in June, would grow as fast in our home-stream as in these foreign waters.

Glancing around me I saw Blackout and the billy-can, but no fishing-net. We were entirely unequipped for any hunting expedition. There was only the billy-can that would hold water, but I devised a plan. . . .

The sticklebacks had all the stream as their playground and I had one billy-can, but I could pit my wits against theirs. Cautiously I stalked the largest shoal, and as I walked along the bank, it made for the darkest corner of the opposite side where a ledge gave shadow. Down there in the gloom hundreds of tiny fishes waited, their fins twiddling rapidly, their small sharp faces all pointing up-stream. But there was another dark place to the left of my left foot. The whole shoal should be enticed to this shadowy cave. Kneeling down I took the billy-can and fixed it carefully in the water where the gloom was deepest. On the bank above I placed the tin lid. The trap was set but would the sticklebacks go into it?

Turning to Blackout I pointed up-stream. "Over," I said. She stood, her head on one side, her whole being alive to the order; then she left me and I watched her ford the stream delicately, taking care not to splash, as I had taught her to do; and she was on the opposite bank, moving deliberately, one step at a time, her Alsatian face absorbed in her task. When she was just over the shoal of stickle-backs, but a yard back, I held up my finger, and she stopped. I beckoned; she crept forward. Head down, tail low, every muscle rippling beneath her shining black flanks, she advanced until her head was over the water. Fish darted from beneath her; myriads of fish. They fled up-stream in one movement that was yet a hundred movements, and I thought they were gone. Then, because I sat motion-less and because the dark depths of the stream were few, they returned in twos and threes to my side of the stream. The leaders hovered over the billy-can; they swam over it, and their bodies were etched sharply above the silver metal: little one-inch strips of fish as quivering as the sixty pounds of bone and muscle standing guard on the far bank. More sticklebacks came downstream, swimming in swift jerks, then stopping to take stock. A bunch of starwort in mid-stream obscured my view of a number, but all at once the entire shoal swept round the weed, and headed for the shadow which housed the billy-can.

Two small fish floated easily through the mouth of the can, and I held my breath. This was foolish fishing; the odds were too far on the side of the fish. The two swam slowly out again before my gaze with a nonchalance that was maddening.

Without moving head or hand I said: "Blackout?"

She did what I had intended her to do—shifted her position, and the fish saw. Dozens seemed to dash into the billy-can; dozens swept under the ledge above the can; and I wondered: is this when I strike, or do I wait for more; for a bigger catch, or perhaps, for none at all? The fish in the can, at least, could not see me; they were in a metal cave, shut in by circular walls of tin. With the lid in my right hand I leaned over; immediately, fish with a clear view flicked themselves out of sight, and I knew I must be quick to avoid a stampede of those now safely inside.

With the lid poised above the water, as one waits before one fires a gun, I waited. Then down swiftly, the water striking cold even on this hot August day, and the lid was against the can. In my excitement I fumbled, and I felt a fish (enormous to the touch under water) slip through my fingers. The lid was clamped into place and I drew the billy-can up.

The first glance inside was a mixture of disappointment and delight. Hundreds of sticklebacks had seemed to disappear into the can, yet hundreds were certainly not in it now. But there were fish in the clear water; several fish, lively and looking almost metallically clean in the unclouded water. I counted them: they stood one above the other, on different layers of water, so to speak, and they had, even in that small space, formed themselves into a shoal. Fifteen sticklebacks, and caught without a net.

We went home then. The billy-can travelled easily with its handle hitched over the handlebars, and the water did not splash out as I had expected it to do. We had gone one mile when the great thing happened: the great event that was to fill our world for two years; that was to make a difference ever afterwards.

We were in the wood, and it was cool at last. Waves of fir needles were blown and had fallen on the side of the track. I dismounted to walk upon them, and to feel their soft dry carpet under my feet. Blackout ran on ahead, loping evenly, and turning every ten yards to see that I followed. The thickly covered branches of the spruce trees formed a ceiling over our heads, a ceiling of tremendous depth in places, but sometimes it thinned and had holes in it so that the sky showed through. It was in the densest part of the wood where we sat at the bole of a spruce; and had I never spilt a fir needle into my shoe we might never have stopped, and then nothing that happened could have happened; or, if it had happened, it would have happened without us.

The bole of the spruce was regular and mighty big: had I put a tape-measure around it I calculated that it would have measured seven feet or even more. The surface was not smooth but scaly, being cut up into hundreds of irregular pieces which roughly fitted into one another, something like a jig-saw puzzle. This fact was important, although I did not know it at the time.

After I had taken off my shoe, emptied out the needles and put it on again, Blackout said: "Come on, have a foot-race. I'll run you to that bramble-patch." So we ran the race, and I lost as I always do, for Blackout can cover the ground like a leaf blown by an autumn gale, when she chooses. We returned to our spruce and I sat down to recover my breath.

Some wood-pigeons cooed away in the wood somewhere, and everything was set as quiet as could be, when suddenly Blackout looked up into the branches above us. "Listen!" she said, and although I could hear nothing at all but the pigeons coo-cooing comfortably among themselves, I did as I was told and listened with all my ears. But I did more: I followed Blackout's gaze. The branches of the spruce were arranged in tiers, and although I could not distinguish more than a few tiers from where I sat, I felt that they went on and on right up to the top of the tree.

Never will I forget how I first saw that red thing sliding down the trunk towards us. My first thought was that this brown blob plastered against the bole high up above us was a fir-cone; for the brown-scaled cylinders of the spruce's cones were hanging in plenty from the tips of its branches. The lump was so high that it had no shape, except that it was long; but whatever fixed it in position up there became unhitched, and it slithered downward a foot or two; and then another yard. Blackout became quite excited and said we ought to do something about it, but as the thing was still fifteen feet above our heads, and the bole of the tree was bare of branches for at least twelve feet, we just watched, hoping desperately that it would not be tugged up again out of sight.

Perhaps it was Blackout's presence that brought things to a climax. She did not bark, for she seldom barked unless I told her to, but she ran up against the trunk, stood on her hind legs, and rested her paws against the bark. With my eyes on the brown thing I did not see what really happened; but all at once a scuttering noise came from the green brushes of the branches (and not from the trunk) and although in one second I was prepared for something to happen, yet I was a little shocked when a russet-brown soft thing fell at my feet.

And stooping down to it I knew what that other brown cone-like object was. I know it was soft too, and that it had life in it and two bright eyes and a puckish face and long, long fingers, and a long plumed tail. I picked up the baby squirrel from the fir needles, and it made no attempt to leap away. Perhaps it was six inches of fur without the tail; perhaps less, but whichever way you look at it, this squirrel was small; and if you take the cone of a spruce as being five inches long and one and a half inches thick, then this squirrel was no more than that.

The little thing snuggled its face into my hand, and then put out a pink tongue and touched my finger with the tip. "Yump!" I said, in baby talk, "Yump, Yump," and after that I thought of him as Yump and nothing else.

I had forgotten the other up the tree, but Blackout had never taken her eyes off it. Calling her to me I thought the tiny thing might regain its courage and have strength enough to climb back to whatever home it had come from. Blackout obediently drew back from the tree and sat down, but she said: "It's not a scrap of use. It'll fall, and if it has to, the sooner the better, and then we can get off home with the pair of them."

She was right, of course. Just then the squirrel became

*"Six inches of fur without the tail."*

opp. p. 14

*The other was still up in the tree.*

unhitched again, slithered downward, made a great attempt to fasten its nails more securely in the bark, but in vain, and dropped further, clawing all the time, until it was level with my shoulder. Its hands and feet were spread-eagled, its tummy was pressed hard and desperately to the bark; but when I put my hand on its back and gently eased it off, it offered no resistance, released its light hold and seemed thankful to be relieved of all responsibility in the matter.

There we were in the wood, nine miles from home, with two baby squirrels. What were we to do with them? No one without irons could have climbed the tree; and if the two had fallen from their nursery, that nursery must have been far up close to the very spire of the tree, perhaps in an old magpie's nest or in the old home of a kestrel or sparrow-hawk.

The one that had fallen last struggled out of my hand and sat on my wrist. Its head was of a lighter hue than the head of Yump—yellower and less red, yet not pale enough to be called real sandy. Something in its face—perhaps in the coy glances of its blue-black eyes—made me think of it as a girl-squirrel. When I poked its side with my finger, it retreated a step and churred indignantly in its throat, and I called it Nuffles straight away; and with the one on my arm and the other lying contented in my hand, I felt I had known these two, Nuffles and Yump, all the years of my life.

Blackout fixed her eyes upon the three of us. She, at any rate, was honest. People say that Alsatians are incorruptible and you had only to look in the honest eyes of her to know this is true. "Blackout," I said "there are times when we are sorely tempted, and therefore need justification for our deeds."

"Yes," she said, her head cocked on one side. "What are you going to do?"

"Well," I hedged, "what we have to find is the justification."

"Ah," she said, running ten paces off, "then let's go home."

It's not as easy as that, I thought; and if I had had a penny I would have tossed for it. My eyes fell on the billy-can, and immediately I wondered how I would carry the squirrels all the way home. My pockets were too shallow; my handkerchief too small. The billy-can was there, but it held sticklebacks. Then I knew what I would do (and it was much harder to do than tossing a penny and calling heads or tails).

We would ride back to the stream, turn the sticklebacks back where they belonged and leave the squirrels at the foot of the tree. If the two were still there when we returned, then we were justified in taking them home, as surely they would die all alone in the wood; and if they were *not* there, then their mother must have fetched them and put them back to bed. There was one flaw in this plan: supposing they had vanished when we returned? Would their mother have found them, or would a stoat or weasel or fox or even a magpie or sparrow-hawk have seized them with tooth and claw? Ever afterwards I might wonder and blame myself and be filled with regret.

Five minutes passed. A light wind shook the firs and showed that the day was changing; and it was a short ride back to the stream and a long ride home after that, and a lot to do. So I built a thick bed of dry oak leaves and fir needles in a deep cup at the base of the tree and put the squirrels into the cup. But I did not cover them with a blanket of leaves for fear the parents might come searching, and not be able to find them.

Then I turned away quickly and hooked the billy-can over the handle-bars and saw that Blackout had already started. And I was somehow not surprised to see that she was striding away in the direction of the stream where the sticklebacks lived, and that her tail, and not her head, was pointing toward home.

## CHAPTER TWO

THE sun was lower in the sky and the stream had lost its shine. Tipping up the billy-can I watched the swirl of water, and in the rings and wrinkles I could not follow where the sticklebacks went. But they were gone. Gone back to the foamless stream, the gently stirring water weeds and the soft, fathomless mud of the stream-bottom. The wind came and pushed at the reed stems, and the stream shivered; and a white cloud rested on its surface, moving slowly until it merged with the bank and was gone; but it was not yet gone, for on looking up to the sky, I found it there still—a small wisp of cotton-wool in a vast setting of blue.

I wiped out the billy-can with dry reed-blades; and then I slowed down like a car that has suddenly been braked, for I must play fair.

The wood was a silent place when we returned to it. I dismounted immediately on coming to the first tree, and walked slowly and sombrely, keeping the excitement well down. But it was there all the same. Two baby squirrels with eager eyes and fluffy tails, and light hearts and scampering ways. . . . What was there but those two—Nuffles and Yump, little red elfs?

The pigeons had ceased their cooing, but a white-throat flitted out of a bramble bush and spoke angrily at us.

Blackout said: "There's a nest in there."

And then we came near to the spruce tree, and I could see it a long way off, for it was a giant tree, even among those giants; and its trunk looked like what men call timber; and the thought struck me that soon men would come with tackle and chains and horses and tractions and saws to cut the squirrels' tree down and to take it away. And they would make an awful big noise, filling the wood with their shouts and commands; and they would spill the tree upon the ground—its beautiful millions of needles; its bark and shreds of its trunk and its massive branches upon which the squirrels leaped. The ground would be covered with the tree all in pieces. And it would be a dead thing, and useful to men; but it would be the squirrels' tree no longer, but matchboarding and weather-boarding and battens and just logs.

I saw that Blackout wanted to talk to me.

"What is it?" I asked.

She rushed away toward the tree, and from where I was I could see her sniffing at the place where I had made the nest. Yet she would sniff anyhow, whether the squirrels were still in the nest or not; so I let myself remain sad, and I thought of the spruce being felled until I was right up there under the tree itself.

Blackout, with her usual courtesy, drew back that I might look, but I could see nothing.

"Put your head down," she said, "like this." And she thrust her long nose into the heap of leaves. I put my hand on the top of the leaves (just as I do when a new litter of my Dutch rabbits has been born in the night and I want to tell by their warmth how they are) and I could feel the warmth that might be baby rabbits or baby squirrels under the palm of my hand. They kicked when I pressed down. Scuffling the leaves apart, I found the pair looking sleepy and friendly. Their little ears were tucked back against their heads, and their whiskers were swept back against their cheeks.

"What is bothering you now?" asked Blackout, seeing how I hesitated.

"Nothing," I said so sharply that she jumped, and in that moment I had made up my mind. The parent squirrels had not fetched them back to the nursery. Maybe they had not noticed the loss of two from a litter of four, five or six.

Gathering dry leaves together I half-filled the billy-can. Then I took Nuffles and Yump and slipped them inside. They slid down comfortably and snuggled close together. Nuffles looked up at me and I thought she winked, but it may have been the way her eyes were made.

Riding through the wood I had misgivings for the first time. Suppose I could not rear the pair; that was an awful thought. All at once I realised how young and frail they were, and I thought back of all the knowledge I had of squirrels; of their ailments and diseases, for things go wrong very easily with our red squirrel, and sometimes years pass before the squirrel population recovers from an epidemic. There was the disaster of 1903 and right on to about 1914 when squirrels died in thousands in the south of England. The population fell very low and the epidemic spread, and soon squirrels were dying in counties farther north: in Gloucestershire, Norfolk and Southern Scotland. The Public blamed the grey squirrel, but very often the decline of the reds occurred in places where grey squirrels had never been heard of. I knew too that red squirrels suffer from bad weather, easily catching cold and pneumonia. The thread of life is very, very slender in all mammals, but in the red squirrel it scarcely seems to exist at all when things go the wrong way. And riding slowly through the wood I grew frightened about what I had done, and wondered whether I ought not to turn back and let them risk their own lives in their own way as nature had intended.

There was night; foxes, owls, stoats, weasels and cold. Worst of all would be the cold and hunger. Unfed, unwarmed, the pair would slip away in the night, and the robins would put strawberry leaves over them in the morning. The wood; the wild wood of the night—such a different wood from that of the day. Rustles behind you and never in front; bumps from everywhere and nowhere at all; and the whispers that you could not understand. Thousands of whispers in the trees and all about; in the leaves and in the soil. Creeping things, whispering; and dark things planning against you in the dark. Eyes everywhere—in every leaf and blade of grass, watching and summing you up, and waiting; eyes that you could never meet. And figures, dark and silent, aloof yet too near, shadowy behind bushes and tree trunks, behind your back and before your eyes; fiendish figures that crept forward on all fours to snatch with fierce glee; figures that worked atrocious crimes in the dark, leaving their work to be seen in the morning. Abominable figures that grasped you and hugged the breath from you and overtook you however fast you ran and ran. And you would trip over bramble sprays, over tree roots, over dips in the soil, and the more frightened you became the more you tripped and stumbled until at last you fell headlong.

Suddenly I realised that I was racing hell-for-leather through the wood, pedalling hard and fast, and that Blackout was galloping beside me, body low to ground, ears pressed down, tail streaming behind; for I had been frightened by my own thoughts and I was racing away from them.

I slowed down, ashamed; I braked; I slid off the seat.

My alarm had been infectious; Blackout looked scared. She ran back and licked my hand and I stroked her head.

"My fault," I said, "but we couldn't ever leave them there to face the night, could we? With maybe nothing to eat and no mother to snuggle against."

I took down the billy-can and peeped inside. Nuffles and Yump were curled close together as peacefully as could be, shut behind walls of tin, and I laughed at seeing them and was reassured. Blackout pushed her long nose into the can and licked them, but neither stirred.

"You've taken on a real job of work," she said, " but won't it be fun?"

We jogged home more slowly after that, and soon were out in the fields again where the rest-harrow grew its pink pea-flowers on the roadside, and the banks were shaven clean by the roadmen for hay. The new haystacks smelt sweet and of the earth; and many were without roofs, having not yet been thatched. One or two had tarpaulins flung over them, and looked like great horses tucked under blankets for the night. The fields were neat and clean-swept after the haymaking; and the aftermath of grass was vivid green, even greener than the fresh green grass of spring that has come up after winter.

Our pace was slow on the last mile. Blackout ran close alongside. "Tired?" I asked.

She touched my hand with her nose. " Just a bit."

I free-wheeled down the drive and she free-wheeled too, rolling effortlessly down as though her legs worked of their own accord. We found a box in the potting-shed; but it was tea-time so we did not wait.

Blackout stood still a moment in the doorway, held in thought. She must have been tired, after all that foot-racing, but she was not thinking of that. She went up to the billy-can, sniffed and asked me to take off the lid. Then she thrust her nose inside, and her whole body was motion-less. She removed her nose and seemed to have satisfied herself about something.

We went indoors and found them all having tea.

"You're late," they said.

I held up the billy-can.

"Whatever have you picked up now?"

"Squirrels," I said, "baby squirrels. Can I have a little milk in a saucer, and does any one know where that fountain-pen filler has been put?"

They all laughed at once and pushed back their chairs.

"Well, have a cup of tea first," they said.

# CHAPTER THREE

WE lay on the grass. The squirrels sat facing each other like two brown goblins. Their ears were without tufts yet; their tails were youthful, but their eyes had a look of experience behind them. Blackout lay outstretched, her fawn paws flung out before her face, her chin resting on her paws. Every now and again when either Nuffles or Yump moved, her expression changed. She was very pleased with the squirrels. She thought they were wonderful. A door banged behind us and she threw herself on guard, casting an annoyed glance over her shoulder. She cross-examined me with her eyes: is this all they will ever be? Where shall we keep them? Do you think they would play with me? What will they eat? Will they be with us all the time—wherever we go? She hit the ground hard with her right paw. The squirrels turned surprised faces toward her. They were seated not more than six inches from her longest toe-nail.

I picked up Nuffles and offered her the spout of the fountain-pen filler which was full of milk. She put her little brown hand over it. "Funny sort of stick," she said, and bit the tip. I pressed the rubber bulb and a drop of milk appeared, hung an instant and then fell upon her paw. "How extraordinary!" she chuckled, and looked Blackout full in the face as though she had produced the miraculous drop. Blackout was delighted. She banged her paw again upon the grass and sighed deep and long. Nuffles took a fancy to Blackout because of the sigh, and flung herself downward, upsetting the fountain-pen filler and tumbling off my lap. Blackout stretched her neck to its fullest extent, licked Nuffles smartly on her off-side, and liking the taste, edged nearer.

Picking up Nuffles once more we tried again. I gently pushed the tip of the filler between her teeth. She bit,

23

tasted the milk, turned a drop over in her mouth and swallowed. She tried again then with more success and drank two long draughts. Then she pushed the filler from her with all her tiny strength, saying that she had had enough. She was quite determined about it. I was sorry she had not drunk more.

Yump was either hungrier or more intelligent. He was at first furious with the fountain-pen filler, and sat scowling at it angrily, but as soon as he tasted the milk his attitude changed. "Nice stuff," he said, and caught hold of the glass with both hands. He had learnt the art then, and I was forced to fill the filler twice with new milk for him. Then all of a sudden, in the middle of a long grand suck, his fingers slackened, he dropped the filler, slid backward and shut his eyes. In alarm, I poked his furry tummy. "How dare you!" he shouted, jumping to his feet; but he was only a little thing, and his wrath was little within him, for he fell back and was asleep.

From Yump's behaviour I argued that Nuffles had not drunk enough to keep a fly alive, but my renewed coaxing ended in a spurt of the stuff falling on her clean snow-white chest. With a rueful expression Nuffles licked herself clean, but she seemed rather cross with me all the same, as though *I* had been clumsy and she had been a proper little lady.

When the squirrels were safely tucked into their wicker-basket, Blackout leaped up. "Now what?" she asked.

"Bed," I said.

We went to bed, all of us together. Blackout lay on her mat on the left side of my bed and the squirrels slept in their basket on the right side. All was quiet throughout the night, but the dawn came early, and I awakened with the dawn (as the parent squirrels awakened out in the wood); and I prepared the meal of milk. The squirrels were sleeping soundly. All they wanted in the world just then was sleep and food. Blackout came round the end of the bed and sat beside us while I offered the fountain-pen filler first to Yump. She was sleepy too and held her ears well down on her head until she saw how Yump drew in the milk in gulps. Then she became suddenly wide awake. Her ears went up; her eyes brightened. She glanced from me to the squirrel and back again. "Gosh, how that little fellow mops it up," she said in amused affection; and I chuckled with her in my pleasure, and stroked her silky head. After his meal, Yump fell asleep again as rapidly as before; just as though I had pressed a button.

But Nuffles would not take the thing seriously. She thrust her hands before her, and separated her fingers as she yawned. She turned her head away from the filler; and I was left with it in my hands feeling worried. "She can't live on air," I said to Blackout.

"I should think not indeed," said Blackout, "The foolish little thing. Should I finish up that milk, do you think, seeing as how they've done?"

"Go to sleep," I said, "it's a long time before morning." But what should I do if Nuffles would not eat?

At six I awakened again, and this time Nuffles drank a small amount, but not enough.

After Nuffles and Yump were curled together again in their basket, I lay awake, wondering. There was something in the feel of Nuffles that I did not like. Yet she was surely the same soft thing. Too soft, that was it. Too soft, and she was not all alight with eagerness as Yump was. She did not clutch at the filler as Yump did; she did not chuckle and gurgle and puff and blow and spill the milk through sucking too hard. Yump was tough. Was Nuffles less tough? Disturbed, I dressed early and went downstairs to warm the milk on the fire.

The green woodpeckers were on the lawn probing the ant-hills with their strong bills. They bowed over the mounds and their crimson crowns glowed in the sunlight. They jerked up and down, down and up, and their light-coloured eyes glistened white in their heads, now here, now gone.

Yump drank greedily at seven-forty-five, and Nuffles woke up and watched him. She licked the palms of her paws, and drew the tip of her tail through her lips, but I imagined that she moved stiffly, and I went down to break-fast feeling baffled and helpless.

All through that August day I coaxed Nuffles, trying to persuade her to drink or eat, but she argued with me, saying that she was not very hungry and would rather sleep, if I did not mind.

But I did mind, and I was shocked at her lassitude.

By the evening Yump was larger than Nuffles. There was no doubt about it any more. In my hand he was small but firm; my fingers closed around fur and limb, and I could squeeze him gently to feel his bones; but Nuffles was boneless in my hand. She was a sponge, and at bed-time I knew that her little body was speaking to me no longer. She sat on her haunches and dreamed, and her tail had lost its power to erect itself over her back, and she was soft as cottonwool right through and would neither eat nor drink.

They said to me: "It will die."

Not yet had I *forced* Nuffles to drink. Always she had drunk the few drops voluntarily; but now she was sinking. She was being starved to death. Soon nothing would save her: not food, nor drink, nor any earthly thing.

I sat by Nuffles and I felt her shadow grow longer and longer over me; and I was sitting in her shadow and not trying any more. Yump slept in his basket but I kept Nuffles on my lap, watching over her, yet doing nothing at all.

They came and told me to go to bed, so I went to bed, taking Nuffles and Yump with me.

Then I wondered why I should be so languid and sit there allowing Nuffles to die because she was just a little thing and had never seen a fountain-pen filler before. I got up and warmed a cup of milk and searched for the brandy bottle in the dining-room.

Six drops of the brandy in the milk, and I wondered what they could do to a sick squirrel. Then for the first time I used force. It was not hard, for she was a light-weight squirrel and had no longer strength to resist; but she turned her furry face away, and said: "Leave me alone. Leave me alone." But I would not leave her alone. Pushing the tip of the fountain-pen filler between her teeth I pressed a few drops of the warm milk into her mouth. She caught her breath. For half an hour I held her quietly in my warm hands. The night had started around the house, but it was shallow and not deep night in the month of August. I fed her again with just a few drops. She swallowed the stuff, but she was not any better. Another half hour and then I forced more drops into her, and this time she took half the contents of the filler.

With Nuffles in my hands I dozed then, and when I came back an hour had gone by. In a fright I clutched Nuffles, having the awful feeling that I held a dead thing in my hands. But life was still in her, and she caught hold of my fingers, and I felt the grip of her nails in surprise that such a little ailing thing could grip so tightly. Again she drank half a fountain-pen filler of brandy and milk, and I wondered where it could all have gone.

Blackout lay beside the bed. Each time I fed Nuffles she sat up and gazed at us long and hard and sleepily, the lids of her eyes falling low over her eyes; and each time we had finished, she lay back and put her head on her paws. We were having a tough fight and Blackout could not help.

All through the night I compelled Nuffles to drink the milk, and when dawn came I fed Yump as well; but he drank eagerly, being impatient for the milk and always ready. Morning came, and Nuffles was still alive.

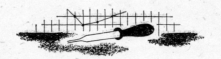

# CHAPTER FOUR

NUFFLES and Yump knew every inch of my room. They knew every tear in the curtains, every mark on the carpet, the shape of every book and the form of every chair. All went well until one day they played hide-and-seek and mistook great-grandmother's Dresden bowl for a tree-trunk. Yump chased Nuffles up the curtains of one window, down the curtains of the other window, across the floor and ran her to ground under my bed. I could hear them squeaking with mirth and rolling over together; and Blackout (who had a good look under the bed before she said anything) told me she thought it was time they were put to bed. They were over-excited, she said. Telling her to fetch them, I opened the door of their house which was hung on the wall above the mantelpiece. In a moment, Blackout had thrust her nose under the bed, and I could see from the slow but deliberate wagging of her tail that she had not the heart to stop their game. Her black shoulders were pushed against the low edge of the bed, and her tail wagged to and fro, as regularly as the pendulum of a clock.

"Fetch, Blackout," I said. "Fetch."

She gave a short friendly bark, and the speed of her tail increased. Frantic scrabbling could be heard under the bed, and then Nuffles appeared, her brown face alight with mischief, one paw held to her white chest, her plumed tail flung cockily over her back. Seeing me beside her house she rushed across the floor, flung herself at my stockings and stopped at my waistline, her face held back, looking up at me, her eyes black with excitement.

"Come on, Nuffles," I said, patting her side.

"Come on, Nuffles," said Blackout in huge delight, jumping on to her hind legs and resting her paws on my shoulder. We were too much for Nuffles. Every one to play with her and all the world her playground. . . .

"Come on then, Blackout," she cried and vanished round to my back, putting the tree-trunk of my body between herself and the Alsatian. Blackout stood her ground. Her face was on a level with mine. She licked my cheek. Nuffles' stock of patience was small. In a moment she was peeping under my arm to see what Blackout was about. "Touch me!" she called, and dashed round to my back. Blackout looked down my shoulder at her. "Funny little thing," she said, "do that again." And Nuffles did it again. Round and round my waist she went, taking a peep at Blackout and then rushing away again in mock alarm.

"Fun, fun, fun!" she laughed, and her eyes were stars of brightness, her ears were pressed back to her head like the ears of a naughty donkey, and her tail hung down behind, beautiful, silky and luxuriant.

Up to now we had forgotten Yump. We were having such a good game, and it was not less fun because we had played it before. Blackout saw Yump first. She turned her head away toward the bed, and Nuffles, with a chitter of delight, leaped on to my shoulder, leaned down and put both her hands, palms downward, upon Blackout's head.

Yump was always a little slower than Nuffles. He was less flighty and more solemn, but he loved a game, and

now he caught hold of my legs, sticking his sharp nails
into me so that I felt them like pointed thorns; and then
he was up too in pursuit of Nuffles. Twice round my waist,
and then the pair found that I was not a big enough tree
for them. Nuffles took a flying leap for the curtains;
Blackout dropped to ground and watched tenderly, her
ears pricked, her eyes fixed on every movement. Yump
followed Nuffles, and the chase was so fast and furious
that Nuffles had no time to think of her next step. She
was forced into a rapid retreat which took her to the
dressing-table where great-grandmother's Dresden china
bowl was. It was all over in an instant. Nuffles' finger-nail
caught the edge of the bowl; her weight, slight though
it was, tilted the bowl up and over, and the crash that
followed caused even Blackout to register alarm.

Silence. The room that had been alive with rushing
squirrels, with flying furry red forms, with the flip of
plumed tails and the jerk of mischievous faces, was suddenly
quiet. Blackout lunged toward the crash and the broken
pieces, and stood transfixed as a pointer dog pointing his
game. Nuffles had been unable to brake quickly enough
and had gone beyond the point of contact to land in the
far curtain beyond the dressing-table, where she now hung
by her finger and toe-nails, her round face turned back
toward us with its scared expression demanding of us:
"What have I done? Oh, what have I done? Was that really
me?" Yump, in similar position on the curtain on the
side of the dressing-table opposite to Nuffles, had his face
toward her; yet the pair could not see each other, for the
table between them

Each of us knew this was a serious happening. Grave
events turn on small items of history, and this was something that none of us could hide or put right. It had
happened. They all, in their own ways, knew this; but
only I saw the small pieces of great-grandmother's Dresden
china bowl, and seeing them, knew that they could never
be put together again.

Blackout's body slackened, and she fixed her grave brown eyes on me. "We've done it now," she said, awe-stricken.

"It's no use crying over spilt milk," I said to them all as I stooped to gather together the broken pieces, but I was sad at heart; and Blackout, knowing this, stepped forward and licked my hand.

Nuffles climbed to the top of her curtain then, and Yump climbed to the top of his curtain, and both squirrels gazed down at the disaster, spellbound, with all the fun washed out of them.

Both squirrels came to bed very quietly then, stepping carefully down on to my shoulder from their perches, and creeping through the front door of their little house without speaking to each other, their faces docile and still scared-looking, as though a death had happened in the room.

Outside, the rain spat against the window panes. Blackout turned her head to listen to the rain, and having listened, looked up to the squirrels' house over the mantelpiece. Then she turned to me, and her eyes were grave. Outside, autumn rain. Inside, red squirrels and Blackout and me. But I saw in a flash how the eyes of Blackout united the two, how the inside must merge with the outside, and how this Dresden china bowl somehow was the key that turned the lock. Neither of us was happy about it; we were uneasy; we were asking the future to be kind to us, without hope, as drowning men beseech the ocean to dry up and be still. Blackout walked to the door, bent her head to the crack, and whimpered in her throat. She stood four-square against the door then, and her raised head was wolf-like and strong, and I felt the strength of her.

"Come on," she said, "better get it over," and I agreed with her and went. . . .

Before the smash of great-grandmother's Dresden china bowl was forgotten, Nuffles and Yump revealed their mischievous skill in another manner, and these two accidents together fashioned the course of their lives in the months to follow. It was November. The leaves of the oaks and the chestnuts and elms had fallen, but the leaves of the ash trees still remained, for, being the last to appear, they awaited a hard frost to pull them down. The song thrushes were devouring the black elder-berries greedily; the blackbirds pecked at the orange rowan berries in desultory manner, being not yet hungry enough to treat them seriously. I collected nuts for Nuffles and Yump and a few late mushrooms from the fields, and the two squirrels thought autumn a grand season, bringing with it not only mist and rain and the first frosts, but bountiful berries, nuts and toadstools, and the seeds of trees to pluck and bury for use in future hard times. I gathered hips from the wild rose bushes in the hedges. Nuffles and Yump loved them best of all.

Searching in my pockets, they discarded the nuts and chose the shiny orange berries, which were elongated and like tiny gay-coloured flagons. One day Yump found a bead on the table which he mistook for a wild rose hip because it was orange in colour. He dashed up the curtain with his find, and sat on the curtain-rail holding the bead in his hands. Nuffles caught sight of the bead and raced after him; and the two chased one another round and round the room until at last I took the bead from them. So Nuffles and Yump could tell one colour from another! Excited at this discovery, I told the Scientists, but they replied that animals can see only black and white and the greys in between. Not satisfied, I chose a brown bead and a black bead, all wooden and all of the same kind and shape as the orange bead; and I laid these three—the brown and black and orange beads—in a row; and I called the squirrels. Seizing the orange bead, Nuffles made off with Yump in pursuit, and not once would either of them test the brown and black beads. But I did not tell the Scientists again of what I had discovered for fear they would put Nuffles and

*Nuffles and Yump knew every inch of the room.*

*"Have Nuffles and Yump done wrong?"*

Yump in the wrong, and say that squirrels could never tell orange from black, not now nor at any other time.

And it was the orange hip of the wild rose and our game with the orange bead that brought upon us our second disaster.

The tube of my toothpaste was orange.

The squirrels found the tube, both of them together.

They said: "Look at this great wild rose hip! Bigger than anything we have ever seen before!"

They bit the tube, and being experts on the insides of things (such as nuts and berries) they agreed that it had a nice soft filling. One of them bit a hole in the tube, and being both excited about their huge wild rose hip, they pushed one another, and bit and scratched; and suddenly the white paste within shot up in a white loop. And one of the pair squeezed the tube with a brown hand. And a toothpaste tube with a hole in it cannot be squeezed without something happening. The paste shot out in relays, more and more, and the more the two squirrels fought and squabbled about this hip of the wild rose, the more the paste came out like a white worm. The squirrels tasted the toothpaste, and one of them liked it and seized the entire tube and leaped over to a chair. The squirrel who was left, followed, and the white worm of paste crawled over the carpet and on the chair and went everywhere with the squirrels, and grew longer and longer.

One squirrel said: "In all my life I have never seen any wild rose hip with so much in its middle."

The other squirrel said: "But it has the wrong sort of taste. No hip ever tasted like this."

And the two became cross with their wild rose hip. They carried it aloft to the curtain-rail, and dropped it, and picked it up again; then took it to the chair, and the bed, and the mantelpiece and the table, and all over the room. And, of course, the white worm snapped and was begun again, snapped and yet again. The two squirrels wearied of the game which had been so exciting while it lasted. They climbed into their little house and their little double bed; and they fell asleep with their arms round each other in their usual manner.

When I came into the room, there they were, two beech-brown squirrels locked in each other's arms, sleeping their innocent sleep.

Looking around the room at the white worm that had so many segments; at the table and the chair and the bed and all those other pieces of man-made furniture, I asked myself: Is this pardonable? Have Nuffles and Yump done wrong? And I knew the answer in my own heart that this was indeed pardonable; and I went quietly to shut the little pop-hole door of their house. . . .

I made excuses for my squirrels, saying that they had mistaken my toothpaste for the hip of a wild dog-rose; but this very argument spoilt my case, for could I promise that they would not mistake a knob on the mahogany chest for a nut, or the upholstery of the chair for the bark of a tree? And I could not promise.

They must go, they said.

Not now, I said. Not in the winter.

And I told them of things in the wild wood that they did not know. Of squirrels in the hole of a tree, and the wind blowing the wrong way, and heaping the snowflakes upon them they slept. What happened to Scott, I asked, and Nansen, and Napoleon before Moscow? They laughed at me, and shifted their chairs closer to the fire, and looked across at one another.

Oh well, they said. Not now then, but they *must* go in the spring. You understand that?

And I went away, saddened—not so much by what they had said, but by this barrier that lies between man and the beast; and quietly I planned what I would do.

# CHAPTER FIVE

IT was all arranged but not yet carried through according to plan.

Mole-hills were conspicuous in the fields, brown mounds against grey-green grass. On the lawn, the worm-casts, thrown up in the night, were miniature mole-hills, over an inch high. The trees were leafless. I went down the gravel path to the log-hut at the end of the garden. The air was damp and clinging.

The log-hut was old but dry. On the brick floor right in the centre was a dusty little heap of moths' wings. Blackout sniffed the heap, interested; but I called her off, for that heap told me more about the moth species of the neighbourhood than all the text books that had ever been written. The bats knew the moths; they knew the fat-bodied moths and the slim-bodied moths, the gaily coloured and the dull coloured. The bats caught the moths under the elms and the sallows and down by the river, and they brought many home to the log-hut to cut off the wings and then devour the rest. I looked around the hut; at the log walls, at the apex roof, and the cobwebs everywhere. The wire windows were intact; the door swung on its rusty hinges. The locker at one side where once the croquet balls and tennis poles had been kept was broken. The house had once been alive and gay; now it was dead.

With a birch-broom from the potting-shed I swept out the floor. I fetched a box and nailed a length of wire to it to hang it from the roof; and there it hung, swinging gently to and fro, and then not swinging any more. Filling the box with hay and the locker with hay, and putting sawdust on the floor, took no time. Blackout helped, and she hindered too.

We fetched a long apple branch from the orchard, dragging it over the grass between the tree trunks. It was too long to be fixed exactly into the length of the hut, so it went cross-wise, and a broken piece jutted out close beneath the hanging box.

This was what I would do, and now it was done.

"Do you think they will like it?" I asked, for Blackout had been subdued all the afternoon.

"Pretty good," said Blackout, "pity, though. We shall miss them."

We walked up to the house without speaking. We fetched the squirrels' little home, brought it down and hung it on a nail close under the roof away from draught. Then I shut the door of the hut and I opened the pophole-door of the squirrels' box. Nuffles poked her head out immediately.

"What's the game?" she asked, and her black eyes sought in every corner of that place for an answer. Yump was pushing from behind; he leaned his chin on her shoulder. The two brown faces peered forth, and suddenly I saw the comic look in their cast of countenance, and I sat down on the locker and laughed softly. Blackout showed her pleasure at this turn of mood by walking over and sitting beside me, just one pace in front. Yump thrust his hand upon Nuffles' shoulders and would have scrambled out, had there been room. Nuffles turned her head. "Stop pushing," she said, "you'll have me outside if you're not careful."

Yump said: "Well, what are you afraid of? *She's* there. They're *both* there. Hurry up, do!"

The two shot out through the pophole-door together, and because there was no other familiar thing in that hut but Blackout and me, they flippetty-flopped across the floor in quick squirrel jumps and leaped to my knees, where they sat gazing up at my face. Two brown elves with tufts to their ears which were outward squirrel signs that they were babies no longer. Nuffles placed one long-fingered hand upon my coat button. "What's the idea? Do tell us."

But Yump was less reflective. Jumping down from my knee he ran across the floor, scuffled experimentally in the sawdust of the far corner, put up his face to the wall of logs, stood gingerly on his hind legs, and pressed both his tight little fists into the fur of his snowy chest. By the nervous jerking of his bushy tail I could see that he was thrilled all over. In the first flush of his excitement he sneezed.

The sneeze, slight though it was, shook Nuffles. "Heh!" she said, scrambling off my knee. "Wait for me."

The two were off together, over the floor, up the walls, down and up and across. Now and again they pretended to be fearful of some monster lying in wait for them behind the logs, or in a corner where everything was as plain as could be. Their pretence was part of the game.

Watching the pair closely, I looked for signs of moult, knowing that a red squirrel moults his body hairs twice a year and his ear-tufts and tail hairs once only. Because Nuffles and Yump were young squirrels they showed no grey on their backs and flanks as older squirrels would have done in their winter coat. They were rufous-brown all over, and their tails were soft and bushy. Next year, in October, they would grow a grey-brown body coat, but still have rufous limbs and rufous tails. Next year? But they were to be with us for this winter only. In the spring they would be gone—wild squirrels. Next year. . . .

After putting nuts in a heap and two apples and a pear on the locker, I went out. The air struck so cold that I went straight to the haystack at the end of the orchard and pulled out an armful of hay. Blackout smelt the grass and said that this would be the coldest night we had yet had; but I replied that I hoped not, because I did not want Nuffles and Yump to have too sudden a change. Blackout said that anyway the field voles were not out feeding this afternoon, and that was a sure sign of frost. Pushing aside the grassy tunnel which she was investigating with her nose, I was forced to agree with her.

Dumping the hay in a corner I looked round for the squirrels. They had vanished. I found them just about to curl themselves round in their old nest-box.

"I've brought in some extra hay for you," I said. Nuffles glanced outside. "Jolly fine place, this," she said. "We like it. And now, I suppose you're wanting to shut pophole-door." But I did not close the pophole, because there was no great-grandmother's Dresden china bowl, nor any toothpaste in an orange tube.

Next morning I knew that Blackout had been right about the field voles. The world was white with frost when I opened the window.

We went out, and Blackout romped with a stick, laying it at my feet as gently as though it had been an egg, asking me to throw it for her. The green woodpeckers were not stabbing at the ant-hills this morning, but one fine yellow-rumped bird flew across the lawn in queer lumbering switch-back flight. After he had disappeared into the copse I heard his rollicking laugh which echoed and re-echoed against the hard walls of the frosted world.

Blackout was down at the log-hut waiting for me to open the door while I was still a hundred yards away.

"Wonder how they are," she said, her nose pressed to the keyhole.

"Very cold for their first night," I replied as I turned the key, and we went in to see an empty room.

"Funny," said Blackout.

She sniffed in the corners, followed a trail across the floor and looked knowingly at the pophole-door above her head.

Anxiously I put my hand through the pophole-door, but at once my anxiety vanished, for there was warmth in there; it struck up against the palm of my hand, and one of the pair within grumbled: "We're quite all right, but we're not coming out to-day—not for anybody."

But in spite of their threats, they came out the next day. The frost had retreated, as frosts so often retreat in December, leaving the air dank and chilly, but damp again everywhere. Blackout and I went into the log-hut together at eight o'clock in the morning. A new moon was still pink in the dusky sky, and the light clouds were pink too.

The squirrels looked as though they had been up some time. They both stood as they were when I opened the door, Yump with one paw uplifted on the nest-box, and Nuffles looking very suspicious on the locker. Seeing us, Yump immediately continued his business at high speed. He disappeared into his house, and from the scufflings I imagined he was making his bed. Nuffles was always more polite, having a great social sense. She hopped over the floor, jumped on to my coat and said: "Good-morning. Any nuts? You've come just at the right time." Forthwith she buried her head in my pocket.

Blackout, who was watching, said kindly to Nuffles: "You chump! Try the other pocket," and Nuffles, finding the emptiness of my left pocket, scurried rapidly round my front to the other. Looking down on her I could see her two hind feet outstretched to their fullest extent, the nails firmly hitched into the material of my coat, and her bushy tail still further extended. Staring at this back view of her, I could see the deep coppery tint of her tail and her hind limbs. Yump was more chocolate in colouring than Nuffles; but this fur so close to my face was vividly alive. Its brilliance made me wonder why I could not pick out squirrels of this colour more quickly in the woods.

A muffled murmur came from Yump in the nest-box. Nuffles heard and Blackout heard and I heard. Nuffles continued gnawing the nut she had found, making hard grating noises as she did so, but Blackout and I glanced toward the nest-box just in time to see the face of Yump appear at the pophole-door, vanish, reappear, and then emerge with an enormous mouthful of hay. Leaping in one bound from the nest-box to the wall, he ran downstairs and thrust the discarded hay angrily into the corner. He sounded so cross that Nuffles threw him a look, but she had reached the kernel by now, and nothing short of a cat would have turned her attention. Yump climbed back to the nest-box, and we could hear furious agitation inside. All of a sudden his tail was pushed through the pophole-door. Within a minute it was followed by his feet which turned themselves backward in the miraculous grasp of squirrels, and seized the outside of the nest-box firmly.

By the discussion that followed between Yump and himself, I formed the opinion that he was very much provoked. His wrathful comments could be heard distinctly by all of us. Once, he sounded to be in acute distress; and wondering whether a mouse had made its home in his bed, I was about to go to his assistance when his animated face appeared at the door. From the black look in his eye I was not unprepared for the sudden skirmish that followed. It seemed to me that his body completely filled the pophole-door like a cork in a bottle, but when a shower of nut-shells, strawy pieces and wisps of hay shot out, I knew that I was wrong.

With all four paws working together, Yump kicked and scuffled. His exasperation was great. I could hear him muttering between each kick: Place hasn't been turned-out for years; I just can't put up with the dust and dirt any longer.

*Nuffles had a great social sense.*

*Nuffles, refusing to follow, told him what she thought of him—*

*—as he dropped to the ground.*

*"Blackout was sitting
beside me . . ."*

And then he sneezed his little coughing sneeze and I knew the dust had gone up his nose.

The violence of Yump's spring-clean was too much for Nuffles. Having finished the last crumb of her nut she left my coat pocket and leaped up to join him. His resentment at her interference was not very flattering, but she kept her good temper until, in the process of turning out the bedding, he came into contact with some portion of her body. The unintended scratch infuriated Nuffles. From the sounds within I think she turned upon him and told him he was a clumsy lout, for in a few seconds Yump fled through the pophole-door, followed by the indignant face of Nuffles. He dropped to ground, and Nuffles, refusing to follow, now that she had told him what she thought of him, disappeared from view.

"You can't turn round when he's in the house," she grumbled, and immediately she set to work at precisely the very thing Yump had been engaged in; but there was this difference: Yump had so nearly finished the spring-clean that her puffings and blowings were mere showing-off. She kept up the pretence for five minutes, but I could see that she was bored by the way she kept passing and repassing the door in a surreptitious manner, hoping for someone to give her the excuse to come out. Not to be outdone she at last hit upon the bright idea of "making an announcement." This she did from the roof of the nest-box. With both hands folded across her chest she surveyed her audience with the air of a practised orator at a political meeting. Blackout was sitting beside me, obviously thinking of something else; and I was sitting on the locker, my full attention on the squirrels; and Yump was in a woody world of his own with a nut between his paws and his white teeth in the kernel. Dissatisfied with the attention of only a third of her audience, Nuffles brought us all back with a jerk by stamping her hind feet smartly upon the roof. As the nest-box was hollow, this action, by even such a very small person, caused sufficient noise to startle all three of us. For an instant Blackout looked up and fixed her whole regard upon the resentful Nuffles; for an instant (but for an instant only) Yump glanced away from his nut and looked curiously at his bedfellow.

In that instant, Nuffles made her proclamation: "I have finished spring-cleaning!"

It was all very nicely timed but I thought I had better put a word in, for she was sitting up there as proud as Punch, with nothing to show but a pile of soiled linen on the floor. So I went up to her and poked my finger in her tummy and she unfolded one little fist and laid her small brown hand on mine. "You know, I *like* spring-cleaning," she said.

"Now look here, Nuffles," I said to her, "All you two have done between you is to turn every morsel of bed-clothing you possess out on to the floor, and you've left yourselves without so much as a pillow-slip to wrap round yourselves when you go to bed to-night. And you're not the sort of folk to enjoy sleeping on bare boards. Now, *are* you?"

She turned her quizzical squirrel look upon me. "Yes, I could just do with another nut," she said. " As far as I can remember, they're in the pocket where the button was but isn't any longer."

And she jumped to my shoulder and thence down.

Blackout said: "She loves throwing her weight about— that little thing, doesn't she?" and she watched Nuffles working upon my pocket with a whole tolerance of affec-tion, because this squirrel was such a little scatter-brain; and that other squirrel too; and it didn't matter a bit really that their doings were erratic, and their moods capricious so long as we had them with us.

But by dusk the pair were sleeping the sleep of the just, and the nest-box was so plumb full of hay that the pophole-door had grown whiskers.

# CHAPTER SIX

WHEN the snow fell, covering the log-hut inches deep, I thought: the days of winter are not long. When the water-dish froze a couple of hours after I had filled it in the morning, I thought: these winter days will pass, and spring will come. And then that thought of spring took my breath away. In the spring those two red furry things must go. I wondered what this place would be like without them. And through the long, long heaviness of winter I was torn two ways. . . .

The Christmas roses in the copse opened their white blossoms, slug-bitten yet ethereal above the leaf-mould from which they had sprung. And I longed for the Christmas roses to last for ever, and not to fade and die away; and while they lasted, I said: spring is far, far away, for Christmas roses do not flower in spring. Daily, as I walked down to the log-hut to visit the squirrels, I looked at each white bloom, counting them, and calling them white nuns, and telling them not to wilt and die. Before the snow, someone had placed bell-jars over the crowns of the Christmas roses; and I scraped away the snow from the glass tents, and peered inside, and I thought of the glass-covered wreaths at the cemetery on the hill. The Christmas roses should have been everlasting too, that spring might never come. The glass domes drew up the stems from the soil longer and longer, so that the flowers were closer to the glass and the light. Every day I saw those white blossoms. . . .

When I heard the robin's quavering voice singing his sad and tender trill, I went back to see that the Christmas roses were still there. I heard the hedge-sparrow singing his spring song too; I heard that thin plaintive warble with misgivings, although I knew it was his custom to sing in the darkest days of winter when the mood was upon him. One day a jenny-wren startled the copse by the vehemence of his song, and I stood still and listened to the outburst, thinking always that with every new song spring was nearer.

Sometimes I was driven to wonder whether I would have the squirrels even at the beginning of spring; for would those two bits of fur live through this hard time until the black ash buds swelled and the grass grew greener every day? There were days when Blackout was unusually quiet in the log-hut; days when she crept softly from wall to wall as though a sick person slept uneasy sleep there and must not be disturbed. On these days I was frightened, for Blackout knew much that was not clear to me; and nearly always she was right in a guess or an intuition, and I was wrong. My anxiety for the squirrels was controlled largely by their appetites, Blackout's anxiety was more deeply-seated; it was an affair of the mind, of the past and the present; and she was armed with tools of cogitation which were far above my faint flickers of makeshift imagination.

In a hard spell of January it seemed that Nuffles and Yump must have passed away. Their banana lay untouched upon the floor, and of all fruits they were most fond of banana. Their nuts—sweet chestnuts and cobnuts—were unpeeled. A pear lay on a ledge, unnibbled. But I would not disturb them, believing that they should have privacy in their nest-box as they would have done in the hollow tree of the wild wood.

Water-pipes froze; the stream at the bottom of the garden was silenced into hard frozen thought; and the starlings waddled across its surface, joking like badly-mannered undertakers as they walked. The cold pressed against the walls of the log-hut, seeming to jam the air inside into solid matter, causing the squirrels' nest-box to be suspended in frozen air. Against this immensity I felt the squirrels could not fight a living battle. The cold would press down upon them, squeezing their ten ounces

of flesh and fur into hard lumps just as it had squeezed far
larger things than Nuffles and Yump. The temperature
had caused the gurgling stream to cease its flowing, and
the water-taps to cease their pouring. Where the snow
had dared to thaw it had checked the drips and turned them
into long icicles, so that no living thing could drink and no
living thing could keep warm. After the third day I flung
an old coat over the squirrels' nest-box, for in the house
they had put sacking and old coats over the cylinder in the
attic; and underneath my coat I put hay as wadding against
the cold; but looking at the uneaten food, I wondered:
am I heaping stuff and more stuff over two frozen corpses?

I brought an empty box, and placing it below the nest-
box I helped Blackout up on to it. And I stood beside her
so that she could reach up and put her paws on my chest.
She understood, and stretched to her full height and lifting
her head, thrust her nose against the pophole-door. She
snorted and her eyes gleamed with interest. She stood on
tiptoe, reaching as far as her limbs would go, and her nose
was telling her all the history of the nest-box, so that she
forgot she was standing on a narrow ledge.

"Careful, Blackout."

She had forgotten me, but she turned her exuberant
face to me, and her eyes were gleaming with what her
nose had told her. She was smiling at my concern, and at
these ridiculous small pinpricks that set me all agog; and
she revealed herself in a swift gesture by licking the cheek
that was nearest to her. She jumped down then, and I was
satisfied.

Two days later Nuffles crept out. She walked stiffly,
hunching her shoulders, and moving her legs with an
effort. Even her tail seemed rigid, as though set in plaster.
Worried at the inflexibility of her entire small body, I
stroked her side, and was at once hurt by the slight movement which removed her from my reach. This was not
Nuffles. But the eyes which regarded me held no recognition. To Nuffles I might well have been a stranger.

There was something constrained about her; something rigorous, unlike the plaything that had been Nuffles in the warm days of autumn. Her eyes had lost their fire and were now sombre. The wild curve of her carefree thought had become formal and unbending. This was not the genial acrobat of the tree-tops and of my shoulder.

Unable to speak with her, I spoke to Blackout: "She has left us. The cold has separated us."

Blackout glared at Nuffles, uncomprehending. "Has she gone old in a week?"

"Not old. Grown-up," I replied.

I offered Nuffles a nut. She looked at me as though I had offered her a tombstone. Her glance seemed to be full of pity. I held the nut out to her as she sat on the roof of the nest-box. My arm ached.

"Nuffles—have you forgotten?"

She lifted her heavy lids, and seemed to examine my face, feature by feature. She lowered her head to my hand.

"This is not me. I am waiting. This is what the cold does to me. Try to understand. . . ."

It was then she made that brave attempt that I remembered for ever. Leaning down with the lethargic stoop of the body which was now part of her, she stretched out her hand and laid her long brown fingers upon my own fingers an inch from the nut. Even that movement seemed too much for her, and a spasm passed over her; but, hoping that I understood this at least, I took the nut from my right hand with my left hand, and gently uncurling her fingers, I pushed the nut against her hairy palm. Immediately her own fingers closed about the nut, so that it was hidden. She drew back, moved her starched little body to the pophole-door and paused with her fingers on the ledge: "You must make allowances, you know . . ." and then she had withdrawn into the bed that she shared with Yump, and I could hear her slowly but deliberately pulling up the blankets.

And it was like that all the cold times; but on warm

days both Nuffles and Yump were rejuvenated. They were
hungry; they were thirsty; they were playful; and they
would have been naughty if there had been anything to
be naughty about.

Watching them leap from the wall of the log-hut to
my shoulder and round and round my waist, Blackout
said: "Quite like their old selves."

But every time the wind went round to the north we
saw the squirrels seldom. They came out once in every
three days or so to eat their apples or nuts, and we knew
only by the food they had eaten that they had been out.

The starlings fizzled more and more on the roof-tops,
threatening to bubble over; and they chuckled and used
worse language every day. The mistle-thrush repeated a
few notes from the blackbird's song over and over again;
and the great tit shouted at the top of his voice, "I sing, I
sing, I sing," until I could have asked him what he intended
to sing. The birds were calling the spring in every hedge
and tree, and I looked back at the receding winter and was
torn again two ways. And I went to see the Christmas roses
which had dealt firmly with the winter with a silent white
capability; and usually I longed for them to continue
flowering until the first crocuses shone golden through the
grass; and this year I besought them from far away to
prolong their season as never before. In that way spring
would be hindered.

All kinds of birds might sing and shake every tingling
bell, and whistle every tuneful note, but as long as the
Christmas roses lifted white blooms from the leaf-mould,
spring was far behind. But when I visited the Christmas
roses this last time, I sought in vain for a single pure
blossom on a green stalk. I visited each plant and probed
down among the leaves, and I found only white knobs on
the surface of the soil that were new unfurled leaves coming
through. And I turned my back on the Christmas roses
and called them Hellebores.

Blackout found the nest of a song-thrush scarcely three

feet from ground level on the ivied wall of the potting-shed. On the dry lining of mud-plaster, four very blue eggs with black blotches rested like jewels hidden away for safety. The mother bird watched us leaning over her nest until her patience gave way and she scolded us so loudly that a blackbird started singing his curfew bell away in the shrubbery, and a wren broke into a torrent of vigorous abuse.

Blackout drew back. "She's angry."

"So would you be," I said, "If you had taken all that trouble to build something out of nothing and then fashion four beautiful blue eggs out of less than nothing."

"You're right. Let's come away," Blackout said.

The thrush's nest was just another token of spring; and soon we found a robin's nest on a hedge-bank where the celandines were glossy yellow, and the nest held five eggs, and no one could run away from the fact that these eggs were not the eggs of winter but the eggs of spring.

Some awkward insidious thing tried to come between the squirrels and me each time I found eggs in a new nest. It came when I saw the first yellow coltsfoot on its sheathed stem, and the first sweet violet on the robin's bank, and the first primrose beneath the hornbeam. It came when the sun caught the crimson rosettes on the wych elm; and it seemed that I pushed the squirrels away, fearing them now that the spring had come. And one day, when Yump clung to my coat like a burr, I gave him a gentle push. "Off, Yump. Get off, get off!"

But he clung there with his nails fast fixed in the cloth, his wistful face upflung and perplexed.

"Are you angry with me?"

"*Angry?*" I brought out, and I stopped and scooped him up so that his whiskers were tickling my chin. "With *you!*"

*" Are you angry with me? "*

*A fledgeling song thrush.*

# CHAPTER SEVEN

NIGHT and day I felt that it had come; and when the first wheatear flicked over the hillside, flashing his white rump in passing, I sat on a gate and thought it all out. The rooks were discussing problems of house-building in the elms; now and again one of them laughed. They were carrying sticks; the old birds were strengthening the walls of last season's nests while the yearlings were erecting smaller cottage-nests. They talked a lot, and the tree-tops were humming with their busy-ness.

The rooks were yet another sign. To-day the signs were too numerous for me to count any more: they came to my nostrils on the light wind from the field and copse; they came to my fingers through every new blade of grass and uncurling leaf of sycamore. And everything the whole world through was a sign, whether I tasted the wind, or touched the new growths, or heard the new songs of the travellers, or the old songs of the residents. And the new days would pass, bringing overwhelming signs that I could not turn away.

So I called Blackout. "To-day we will go to Badgers' Wood, and we will take them with us."

For the last time I closed the pophole-door. Nuffles and Yump were shut inside; and I unhooked their little house from the wall and tied a rope around it for a handle. We went outside, and we walked a long way all down by the stream and across many fields. Blackout ran on ahead, never going far and often returning to sniff at the squirrels' box and me. The cock chaffinches were repeating their spring peal of cheerfulness over and over again, and when I looked about for each bird, I saw him resplendent in his new suit, his breast gaily rose-coloured; and the white bars on his wings were striking and could be seen a long way off. The hedges were alive with tits, just as though feathered mice had built their holes in the twigs; and I saw blue tits, like wisps of blue cottonwool, and great tits with great dabs of Indian ink on their throats, and cole tits that were smaller than the great tits, and then a single pair of long-tailed tits in a birch; and I could see them all because the shrubs were thin and scantily clothed.

We came to Badgers' Wood, and having come I could not go in at once. I must put it off. So we walked around it, and the wood was larger than I had thought, when you examined it that way; and an hour had passed quickly and still we were not back at the place we had started from. All around the wood great fields stretched; and looking over the fields, you could see no other wood at all. At one end the wood was tilted up on a slope, and that was where the badgers lived. Their great holes led down into the earth, and you could see by the marks in the bracken which were badger-roads, and which were just nothing at all. I sat and watched for a while and saw no badgers; and then I heard one, and it was as though I were listening to a silent footfall. But to-day my vain cry was not to know badgers, nor tits nor chaffinches, nor anything that I could put a name to; and I was shocked at my own self when I rose from the bracken, having heard the badgers, and picked up the little box and passed on.

Inside the box I felt Nuffles and Yump scrabbling in the

hay, for it was day and they were unaccustomed to being shut in their nest-box at a time when every one else in the world was about some business or other.

Blackout said: "What do we do now?"

I said: "Oh, Blackout, I forget, I forget."

Blackout said: "Sometimes I disremember too."

And I thought what a wonderful dog she was to disremember and to tell me just like that, how she disremembered; and I was not alone any more.

The wood was an island in a sea of grass. Perhaps Nuffles and Yump would stay in this wood and never set sail on that green sea, and then I would know always where they were. That was the thought I had; but now the wood seemed a forest, and indeed, to a squirrel it would be the mightiest forest, and if to a squirrel, then to me too. After all, I could know only the ground-ways—the trackless ways between bramble and bramble that meant no more than a bush here and no bush there. But the mouse-runs were real paths, tiny pathways that were sometimes tunnels through the underfelt of the wood's floor, and sometimes faint tracks beaten out by the lightest of feet. Long-tailed field-mice would be there with paws in white kid gloves; bank voles with paws less pure than the long-tails; and field voles too, who are the duskiest of all. The tracks of these, if I followed them conscientiously, would lead me to the holes underground; and I would know by the marks on the doorstep whether a hole was inhabited or not. The half-bitten kernel of a sycamore seed, the left-over blade of grass and the morsel of newly-turned soil—all these would tell. And I would read the artless signs of the weasel and stoat, and the plain tale of the hedgehog; but how could I follow the squirrel-roads aloft in the tree-tops? In the strange land of twigs and branches and stout trunks and everywhere leaves flapping against leaves, I would be lost. But Nuffles and Yump would know every lane and every gateway. The roads would change with the seasons; new growth would block main staircases and fashion new ones, and the squirrels would leap in winter where in summer the foliage would force them to bye-pass this and that.

Down on the ground I would read a little of the squirrels: nutshells, peeled bark, a wisp of red fur, but never could I know those squirrel corridors high up in the trees. When I opened the pophole-door, the pair would climb all in a moment far out of reach, where they would not listen to my call, but wander like winged-birds from tree to tree away from Blackout and me who must ever remain with our feet on the soil—earth-bound.

Coming to a place in the wood where the softwoods gave way to the hardwoods, we stopped beneath an oak. Oak neighbours stood all around, but they had spaced themselves out; and looking down at the tufty stuff at my feet I saw the withered grey capsule of a bluebell, and saw at once how this clearing was misty blue in bluebell-time. I saw honeysuckles then under the oaks—honeysuckles that tried to throw their arms around the trunks, and falling, stood there with their arms uplifted. The mesh of the honeysuckle twigs, crossing and recrossing in a tangle, was thick enough to hide the nest of a dormouse six or twelve feet from ground level; but the dormice would be scarcely awake yet, for their winter sleep is long.

"This is their country," I said, and Blackout ran back to listen to the news, but that was all just then, for the pophole-door must be opened. Nuffles put her head out. She sniffed the air, her pink nose wriggling daintily. Yump scrambled over her back and was outside on the grass before he meant to be. He stood there, transfixed.

"Look!" Blackout cried, "he's scared stiff!"

His ears were hard back, his eyes were as the eyes of a bolting horse, his tail gave spasmodic, nervous jerks, and his little fists were clenched to his chest. Suddenly he rushed back through the pophole-door and vanished from sight. I could hear him scrabbling in the hay in the far corner. The shock had been too great for him; he was hiding his head and his body too, burrowing deeply into his familiar hay. Yump's retreat frightened Nuffles who withdrew from sight. I waited. The box held two silent squirrels. They were not sulking; but they were alarmed at this upstart world, this vast universe that was suddenly too spacious for them, that held too enormous possibilities.

But their move was unexpected.

Blackout slipped across and sat beside me, looking amused, I thought. "Your call, pal," she said, and she waited, watching us both—the box and me.

"What do I do?" I asked her.

"This," she answered, and she ran a few steps off, fetched a short stick and laid it at my feet.

"All right," I replied, "Good—we'll play while we wait."

We played that dog's old game of fetch, and I flung the stick far away between the oak trees, and Blackout fetched it again and again. And still the squirrels did not stir. Blackout was the first to tire of the game, and I was surprised; but looking at my watch, I saw we had been playing a long, long time.

Taking the squirrels' box, I shook it gently. No one moved. Then I put a hand through the pophole-door and I felt someone soft and warm at the tips of my fingers. But that did not shift them.

"Blackout," I said, "We are bound to this spot for evermore!" And we sat down and waited.

A sparrow-hawk whistled through the clearing like a rocket, and I thought again of the dangers that Nuffles and Yump must face. A jay yelled harshly, and flew to a nearby oak tree and said a lot at us but nothing to us. A shrew in the grass tuft close to my feet spoke to a chum in a lisping voice. A treecreeper ran up the trunk of a tree with the nimble ease of a mouse; he went round the bole in spirals, and every time he crept round from the far side his breast gleamed white; and he was so near that I could see the curve of his tiny bill.

Blackout lay outstretched on the grass. She was not asleep, and every time a new sound came out of the wood, she opened her eyes, but did not move her head.

Sitting there in Badgers' Wood with the wild birds in the trees and the little scuttling animals of the grasses, an impossible hope suddenly came to me. And having come unbidden I wondered why it had not come before. . . . Perhaps after all I would not say good-bye to Nuffles and Yump to-day. Possibly—just possibly—I would see them again. I would leave them *in their own little house* in the wood. . . . And although I called this wishful thinking, I immediately took the box by its handle and set off for a great oak facing me. The trunk was thick with ivy and one branch was so low that it almost caught my head as I walked under it. In a moment I had grasped the bough and swung myself up, box and all, into the tree. I was in a new world, for just above my head, as I stood erect, I found a wedge between the trunk and another branch, and this wedge was filled with the glossy leaves of ivy. Untying the rope, I fixed the box in position with the pophole-door facing south, and I tied it securely in place with wire and rope, that not the mightiest wind might dislodge it.

The tree was enormous all about me and I felt very small, and I wondered how small a squirrel would feel. There was nothing to do then but to climb down, but I had not pictured it this way, and I sat there hesitating. It was worse going away without seeing them—just as though I were forsaking them, like leaving Moses in the bulrushes. It all seemed wrong, yet I was sure it was right, and then they could shift for themselves, and they would always have a home to go back to.

"You are a coward," I said, swinging my legs to and fro from the branch; and then I knew that, being a coward, I had waited too long.

That intimate touch on my shoulder was a caress. Her whiskers were against my cheek before I had looked round.

"Nuffles, Nuffles," I called her, and twisted her tail around my finger, and could not tell what to do now. She was in my pocket in a moment, searching for the never-failing nut; and there we were, the squirrels and I, in the oak tree, with all the age-old trees around us and the scanty spring ceiling above us, and all the birds calling and singing how wonderful was the keen clear call of spring. And I could have sat there for evermore, had I been something other than what I was.

She sat on my shoulder. She—this lively red sprite— was motionless, thoughtful. Gazing before her, she heard the voices of the woodlands, but she gave no sign that she heard the songs of the wild birds and the whish of the wind through the leaves. She crouched low on her haunches, her shoulders hunched. Her ears were still tufted; but looking sideways at them I could see that she had begun to moult those long pencils of hair. By June her round ears would be smooth, but now she was still a child of winter.

Had I said to her: "Sit by my side before I go," I would have been ashamed somehow, as though I asked for something that did not belong to me; but now I was proud.

Had I said to her: "You are free. Stretch your wings and fly away," I would have wronged her, for with her wistful look upon me she would have asked: "What is this freedom that is in your mind?"

Had I said: "Good-bye," I would have separated myself from her, and marked myself with the piteous farewells of humanity.

There should be no good-bye; and presently I touched her lightly on her side; and she turned her head and took my finger gently between her teeth, thoughtfully, as one who dreams sweet dreams and cannot return to reality. Lifting her from my shoulder I set her on a branch, and she watched me calmly as I turned my back on her and slid down the tree to the ground.

I would not look back.

But I heard the swift scamper of her jumping through

the honeysuckle, and felt the clutch and cling of her nails on my legs and on my coat. She swung round my wrist and was before me, her head flung back and her lips parted in her quaint rabbitty face.

" *Nuffles!* "

And I saw the sly twinkle in her eyes and the laugh in her as she rushed round and round with my hand in pursuit. The game was so fast that she was panting and I was out of breath; and she was all smiles and naughty behaviour. And I played her game right up to the end until she was tired and ready to sleep in the nest-box that was her home. And I never knew that I was crying until I could not see her any more . . . and after that she was gone through the pophole-door . . . and I felt Blackout's cool touch on my hand, and I leaned down and put my arms around the strong shoulders of my dog.

"*I set her on a branch.*"

"She was all smiles

*d naughty behaviour."*

"She leaned over, peering at me."

## CHAPTER EIGHT

Next day I returned to Badgers' Wood and I climbed up to the nest-box. No one was within, but the hay seemed warm to my touch. Sitting under the tree I heard the first call of the migrant chiff-chaff ringing through the woodland: "Chiff-chaff, chiff-chaff, chiff-chaff, chiff!" Seeing neither chiff-chaff nor squirrels, after a while I returned home. The following day I came again, and the next day, and the next; but always the little house in the oak was empty. The week afterwards I came on an evening as dusk fell. The blackbirds were chinking in the bushes, and a brown owl called three times from a fir. Blackout said: "Look at that rabbit, cheeky beggar. Just *look!*" and her tail wagged in dignified rhythm to and fro as she watched the rabbit that she knew she must not chase.

I climbed the oak for the seventh time, and I noticed how some of the ivy-leaves had been worn away by my climbing. I put my hand on the box, and the solid feel of the box told how they were within. And I remembered the seven nights and days and thought how foolish I had been, but this time I climbed down again just as before, without disturbing them, for it was dusk, and a squirrel must wrap himself round with his bushy tail when the sun sets. Emptying my pockets of nuts I left the pile at the foot of the tree and went home.

The next day I came to Badgers' Wood an hour earlier. Half an hour passed. A bat flickered like a shadow between the trees and was gone. Perhaps the squirrels were already in bed; yet I would not climb up until dusk had truly fallen.

He was there, and I had not seen him come. . . . Sitting on the lid of the box with one hand held up to his white chest in the old familiar way. And in one minute she was with him. Nuffles and Yump together on the roof of the nest-box as I had seen them a hundred times before, yet in such a different setting. They looked down at me, and their silly tufted ears made me think their eyebrows were raised. I might have been a cow. Sitting very still I gently rattled the nuts in my pocket. They were curious, and Nuffles took a short step forward. I might have been a sheep. I spoke to them in the language they knew. Yump flung his hands over his head, drew his ears down to his eyes, then licked his palms and rubbed them together. This was Yump; and forgetting how our surroundings were changed I rose to my feet that I might watch him washing his hands as of old.

He threw me one look and slipped quietly through the pophole-door. I stood rigid. He had turned his back on me. He had sent me away.

No sooner had he gone than Nuffles ran down from the nest-box on to the branch above my head. Leaning down, her hind feet grasping the branch and her head below the level of the bough, she looked hard at me and said: "What on earth are you? We don't want any sheep and pigs around here." And I stood stock still, fearing to move a muscle and send her away, but I did not mind being a sheep or a pig or both together, for she was near enough for my hand to touch, had I put it up to her. She leaned over, peering at my head and scrutinising my hair for what seemed a long, long while.

Another bat tripped through the air and I thought: time is short.

All of a sudden she drew back and swung there, as light as thistle-down. I thought she too had gone and I dared to look her full in the face that I might at least watch her go. Her eyes were black as boot-buttons and shining and curious, and her little brown face was just as comic as it had been in the log-hut, so I smiled; and smiling at Nuffles, I heard the swift patter of paws and the slithering scuffle of a squirrel leaping through a tree. And it was a strange thing how Nuffles and I looked each other in the face and neither turned our heads when that slight red figure swept through the ivy leaves. Yump landed lightly on my shoulder. Swiftly then their shyness passed as a drop of dew dries under the morning sun; and Nuffles, not to be outdone, followed Yump, and I felt the pressure of their tiny hands on my neck and my coat and my hair, and scarcely knew where either was from one moment to the other beyond that they were on my person like Lilliputians tugging at Gulliver's beard. They discovered nuts in my pockets, and a piece of biscuit that I had not known was there, and the rind of a cheese that was hoary with age, and a piece of string.

The barrier that the wild wood had erected between us was down and we were as we had been in the log-hut.

Out there in the wood I seemed to have captured a dream; and the miracle of feeling the cool touch of their paws and the tickle of their whiskers made me wonder if indeed I were one part squirrel. No flower could fade, no lamp could go out, while this recognition between man and squirrel existed in the wild wood. I pressed Nuffles to me and felt her slight frame move warmly under my hand as she slipped away to my waist. I clasped Yump between hands that never meant to hold, and felt the giggle of mirth pass through him as he thought he had eluded my fingers.

We heard the chiff-chaff and the blackbird and the swift breathing of ourselves, and the rustling of the leaves over our heads and on every side; and we were part of the wood as were the whispering leaves and the flying birds. Then suddenly the dusk of the wood changed the mood of the squirrels, and through them, the mood of me as well.

Nuffles said; "Goodness, I had no idea it was so late."

Yump said: "Just shows how you forget when you begin playing high jinks."

They ceased their games and strayed from me like children called to bed; but they went reluctantly and slowly, stopping on their way to wash their hands and part the hair of their tails; and I watched them go without regret and without desire to be consoled, for they had singled me out and set me higher than a pig, or a sheep, or a cow.

# CHAPTER NINE

EVERY day I walked the two miles to Badgers' Wood, carrying nuts and fruits to put under the oak tree for the squirrels. I had never seen any other red squirrel in this wood and I believed Nuffles and Yump to have the wood to themselves. In the early mornings the pair seemed to travel far through the tree-tops, leaping up to the pointed tops of the firs and diving perilously fast through the green depths of the oaks. The trees shouldered one another in the wood so that some were kept dwarf and never allowed to attain their natural height; and the closeness of the trees made a dense jungle to hide a baboon or a gorilla or a squirrel; and it would have hidden each one of these for a month and a year.

Nuffles and Yump had only to plunge a little way into the forest and they were lost. Even in March and early April when the leaves thinly clothed the deciduous trees, the squirrels could vanish in half a dozen bounds. On wet days the two slept most of the day through. Like cats, they hated wetting their paws. In a wet spell I often did not see them for days, for they ate their dinner in the early morning and then retired to bed. We had sunny spring days too. Blackout found new nests in the wood and fetched me to show them to me. Every day new migrant birds arrived, and I heard their voices always before I saw them flying. The primroses were scattered like thousands of yellow discs on the banks; and their leaves were crinkled and fresh and I put my face right into the heart of the primrose plants to smell their scent. Sometimes an Orange Tip butterfly flitted along the bank; and the Small Whites and Green-veined Whites awoke in the sun. The swallows came, twisting and turning over the fields with their forked tails displayed; and the House Martins too, showing their white rumps wherever they flew.

The birds could come from distant lands and the butterflies could hatch from their chrysalises, and I could watch their coming, but always I myself was with the two squirrels. I knew that I was waiting for something to happen to them. Was I afraid that they would shift their quarters? Or that a brown owl with owlets to feed, would be tempted by ten ounces of flesh and bone? But I did not know what dreadful thing could be waiting round the corner. Perhaps it was all imagination and we would go on like this for evermore. Sometimes I found myself hurrying over these two miles. One day I even ran the last hundred yards, and was satisfied only when I was met by a swiftly racing Nuffles who flung her small form at my legs.

The first call of the cuckoo distracted me, for the oft-repeated voice was clean and fresh, without inner disturbance. Fledgling song thrushes hopped over last year's leaves and gaped at Blackout with their froggy mouths and gawky faces. Fledgling mistle thrushes, greyer than the song thrushes, hopped through the thickets; and other fledglings came: robins and blackbirds from early clutches of eggs. The ponds were dizzy with their tadpoles—frogs, toads and newts, and all the jellied frog spawn had disappeared. Yet with all these movements the life of the squirrels seemed to stand still.

Within the wood I saw the trees as though I stood within a room and could not see the outside of the house, but when I came to the edge of the wood from the field, I saw the calm beauty of the flowers of trees. Most of the flowers were greenish in colouring and wonderfully fashioned in intricate pattern. The catkins of the birch, having hung ready since autumn, flushed a deep dark crimson; and the alder catkins were red and red-brown too. Every day new flowers came from the trees until the beeches blossomed, the oaks, ash, poplars and aspens. The floor of the woodland was carpeted with wild anemones, white and starry. A pied flycatcher flew through the wood, making his way north, a pierrot in black and white. His more sombre wife followed after, and the two chatted to each other in voices that were like white chips of wood cut by the axe. The slim willow-wrens and cocky whitethroats were among the first arrivals. They appeared all at once in every thicket and bramble bush, and once they had arrived we were not without them any more. The early morning was the chorus of birds, each trying to out-sing the other, and the noise was so loud and the business of the day so considerable that I awaited some sign from Nuffles and Yump, who gave no sign beyond friendliness and fun and chat.

One day Blackout said: "Come and see what I've found." She led me to a bank where the last bluebells were dying. She sat down, turning her brown eyes from me to the bank and back again, as proud as Punch. Suddenly I understood her meaning. A willow-wren's nest. It was a dugout in the bank, a hole that was filled with feathers. Blackout watched intently as I put in my fingers. It was her nest. Her find. She had learnt the crime of birds'-nesting and the joy of birds'-nesting without breaking a single egg or hurting a single nestling; and now she was an honourable Alsatian showing off the treasures of her patient quest. I put two fingers through the entrance of the nest and felt tiny eggs—four, five, six. Cautiously I withdrew an egg. It was nearly round, and on its delicate white shell were reddish-brown speckles on the larger end. It lay on my palm. Blackout, with careful deliberation, pushed her black muzzle over my palm until it was an inch away from the egg. Something told her that she must not even lick this precious thing. Throwing at me the saintly look she might have given me in a church, she reverently withdrew, and watched in devout silence as I replaced the pearl in the nest. As we went away we heard the plaintive voice of the willow-wren giving thanks for our withdrawal.

Everywhere the houses of the wild birds were sheltering eggs. The whitethroats had built in the brambles deep cups with walls of fine grasses so fraily felted that they seemed to be fashioned for one day only. The greeny-blotched eggs were laid and we were in mid-May.

The weasels and the stoats, the shrews and the field-mice were with young; the birds had their nests and the woodland was gay with flowers; and I glanced up at the pophole-door of the squirrels' house in the oak and was shocked that I should have cut their wings by setting them on a desert island.

Blackout found the twin eggs of a nightjar on an open bracken-covered slope of the wood. Queer-shaped eggs they were, having neither big end nor little end, but they were beautifully blotched with liver and lilac on a whitish shell, and were laid on the bare ground without any pretence of a nest. I congratulated Blackout.

"Jolly good show," she said modestly.

And knowing how the nightjar is one of the latest migrants, I looked behind at the winter-spring that was already past instead of at the summer-spring that was still to come, and I was sad where before I had been glad that in all this space of Badgers' Wood two squirrels, and two squirrels only, were passing the days away in frolic and fun. And I fell to wondering how long a red squirrel lived. Perhaps three years, perhaps four; but with all the dangers of the wild wood I did not allow Nuffles and Yump more than another winter and spring. Then they would be gone. One first and then the other, and the woodland would be as it had been for years—without red squirrels, but with badgers and foxes and stoats and weasels.

A dead-end.

The migrants would come and go. First the willow-wrens and whitethroats and chiff-chaffs and swallows. The house martins and blackcaps and nightingales would follow after; and the swifts and nightjars and spotted flycatchers last. They would come and wander through thicket and tree next year just as they wandered in this; and if the whitethroat in that bramble was a different

" . . . *passing the days in frolic and fun.*"

*"Everywhere, the houses of the wild birds were sheltering eggs."*

whitethroat from the one who churred there to-day, he would be a son and therefore the same bird.

Nuffles and Yump. Where was their beginning that was but an ending?

Should I take them one day away from this wood and carry them back to that other wood miles away where they had been born? Should I untie their box from its moorings in the oak and carry it away and hitch it to the handlebars of my bicycle and ride away, and so leave Badgers' Wood bereft of squirrels?

I asked Blackout: "What shall I do?"

"You think too much," Blackout said. "Leave them alone." She kindly fetched my stick for us to go home. . . .

The whole of May I pondered the justice of isolating two squirrels in a wood where every mortal creature was building a home and rearing young. Where every living thing was on the increase. The whole of May Nuffles and Yump played in their oak tree, making excursions where I could not follow them, but always returning at the time appointed to receive their nuts and play hide-and-seek on my old coat. And any day I could have pushed them inside their box and closed down the pophole-door, and carried them off to a wood where they might have met their father and mother squirrels and their brothers and sisters. Any day I could pick up their furry bodies and transport them to a far country. I could kidnap Nuffles and Yump now just as I had kidnapped two baby squirrels in August last year.

The spotted flycatcher took to himself an outpost in the clearing and sat all day long on a knob from which he made short swooping flights after moths. His wife sat in her nest in the crook of an ivy clinging to an oak. This was *my* find. Blackout had missed it as it was above her head, but I pointed it out to her that she might know for another time. The cock had helped to build the nest, and I had watched him while the squirrels romped around me in the clearing, hiding their surplus nuts under dead leaves.

Now the cock had earned his rest. He was having a lazy time while his wife brooded their four eggs. The snap of his beak was audible in the clearing from morning until dusk. Next year he would be sitting on his stump again, dashing out after flying insects in spectacular attack and then returning to sit in depressed attitude on his landing-ground. And if not this flycatcher, then his son. Their steps would go on, year after year.

The spotted flycatchers were the last to build. That brought it all home to me. They were the latest of the migrants to build a nest and the latest of the residents. Other birds—blackbirds and thrushes and hedge sparrows—would build second nests and rear second broods, but they had all started earlier. The spotted flycatchers were unlikely to have another brood unless an accident happened to their first. And I knew that the period of nesting and rearing young—the time set aside for increase of the race—was drawing to a close.

Looking at Nuffles and Yump in their short-haired summer suitings, I was unaccountably depressed. It was no longer enough to sit and watch them: to see how they had moulted all the hairy pencils on their ears and were now with rounded clean-shaven ears; to see how the dense fur of winter had been thrown off for a thinner coat to take its place; to see their bushy tails less bushy than in winter; to see how the palms of their hands were naked again and no longer hairy as in the winter months.

"What does it matter," I said to Blackout, "if Yump's hair turns grey with age and his eyes grow dim, and Nuffles sees him as an old squirrel, and he sees her as an ageing squirrel with the fun gone from her? What does it matter if their limbs stiffen until they can no more leap up to that oak branch or dive down to the ground with the ease of winged animals?"

Blackout said: "It doesn't matter a scrap. We must all grow old. It is easier than you think." But suddenly she changed her mind. "Oh, but it *does* matter to you," she said, and she lifted her paw and placed it on my knee and looked hard in my solemn face. And then she unreasonably whined.

"We will fetch them to-morrow," I said to her, "and take them back to the other squirrels to the wood where they belong."

But when we returned the next day, the nest-box in the oak tree was empty; and when I put my hand in through the pophole-door, their bed was cold.

# CHAPTER TEN

AFTER an hour of searching in the trees and thickets, Blackout said: "What's the hurry?"

Had I been hurrying then? I had run from one tree to another, from bramble to thorn, poking, peering, and running back to the tree I had already searched; and my haste was the haste of the person who is panic-stricken. I could not say: "They will come home," and be honest. They were gone. Knowing that squirrels can travel many miles in their search for new hunting-grounds, I had no hope of finding them. Yet I sought them high and low, walking miles through the wood and the fields, calling to them, "Nuffles, Nuffles, Yump, Yump!" while Blackout's brown eyes shone with excitement and she said: "What's the hurry?"

The whitethroats churred at us from the brambles, the willow-wrens sobbed from the hazels; and the wood seemed to hold a nest in every yard. At last, tired and foot-weary, I said: "It is ended." And Blackout came and smacked my knee hard with her great paw. "Buck up, old thing," she said.

My feet were tired, and we turned back through the wood. From craning upward, my neck ached, for more often I stared into the trees than on the ground, longing to see one red galloping figure up there aloft. We returned to the clearing of oaks. As a last hope I climbed up to the nest-box and put in my hand. The box was deserted. It would never hold Nuffles and Yump any more. They were gone. Flashes of danger: stoats, foxes—but the box was out of reach of any animal but that ancient enemy of red squirrels, the pine marten. And there were no pine martens; nor had there been for many, many years.

We sat on our old seat on the grass where we had full view of the nest-box in the oak, and Blackout suddenly said, as she had once said before in this same clearing: "Let's play," and she fetched a stick. I forgot the time, but we must have been in Badgers' Wood the whole day, and then all at once it was the afternoon and the hour when we always came, day after day, to feed the squirrels and play high-jinks with Nuffles and Yump. It was that very same time. Without looking at my watch I knew this. Habit is strong, and when a beautiful custom is broken by the other party, you are saddened and bereft. You have dropped your torch in the darkness and you cannot find it again. The hour pressed down on us and we stopped playing. Blackout ran soft-footed into the dense wood out of the clearing; she was searching with her muzzle to the ground. A magpie croaked. The big bird was up there in the squirrels' oak, a long bird in black and white with an over-long tail. He swung his tail up and down in easy motion, but I thought how heavy it was, that tail, and then I was cross with the magpie for perching near the squirrel's box. That cruel black beak, so strong, like a chisel. He was a hard bird. He would devour fledglings, seizing them from their nest, throwing them into the air and gulping them down. A magpie would suck eggs, devour anything that crossed his path, but surely not a squirrel? Was it on record that a magpie had ever caught a live squirrel and pecked its brains out? A sick squirrel perhaps, but never a squirrel in full possession of its senses; and I could not imagine even in this dark moment that Nuffles and Yump would be killed by this top-heavy bird.

But my mind was too ridiculously narrow, I had found a link between magpies and squirrels, but it was the wrong link. Had I considered the magpie and the squirrel with a smile instead of with grim death in my heart, I would have organised my searchings on a different footing and have climbed the trees instead of walking and walking on the ground. My heart was still black with hatred and suspicion of the magpie when it happened. . . .

It was one of them—either Nuffles or Yump—leaping swiftly down from a gnarled oak not six yards from where I sat, and scarcely believing my eyes, I jumped to my feet and shouted at the magpie: "Get away, you! Get away! Shoo!" The magpie flew off, but not very fast, and I breathed a sigh of relief and I looked for the squirrel. No squirrel was in sight. I had frightened it away just as I had scared the magpie. Neither Nuffles nor Yump were accustomed to my shouting. Indeed, they had never heard me raise my voice. No wonder I had put the fear of evil into that red gliding figure.

One glimpse and no more. They were gone. But they were alive.

If one, then why not two? Nuffles and Yump must have moved house by mutual agreement. The day had been well spent after all. It was natural that I should walk over to the spot where I had seen what I had seen. Blackout came too but she could not help; it was off her beat.

The tree had a giant head as though it were pollarded like a willow. Earlier in the season a great tit had reared his young in a hole, and had made a tremendous to-do about the feeding of the brood. Long since he had led the noisy youngsters away; but on remembering the great tit's nest I remembered too the old magpies' nest that I had found higher up in the head of the oak. It was the usual domed affair, probably three or four years old, for the mud-cup where the eggs had been laid was a heavy thing weighing several pounds. Almost before I had looked up at the magpies' nest I knew that *this* was their new home. Standing at the foot of the oak, the nest seemed far away, for it was densely screened by one thing and another: ivy leaves, oak twigs and the like. But it was no more than eight feet from the ground, and I thanked my stars that I myself was near to six feet tall. By sticking my toes in the twisty ivy at the base of the tree I could raise my face on a level with the nest.

There was no need. She was up there grinning with the mischievous gleam in her eye. "So you've found us out?" she said.

The relief of it, to know that it was not the end after all. "Which of you is it?" I asked.

"Me, only me," she said.

"It would be," I replied.

They both were there, and they required no coaxing to come down. Of course, it was their accustomed time, and a squirrel is a creature of habits. It was lucky that the door of the magpies' nest was this side, and I was able to put in my hand and feel the hard-caked mud that would need many gales to shift it from that tree.

Mud for a bed, and they were used to hay.

They pattered out of the tree and across the grass, and they had gone this journey many times already. I could see that. Running straight to their old oak, they bounded up to the nest-box. They had some definite plan, and whether it was bed-making or the collection of food, I could not tell. Their industry was extraordinary; yet they accomplished nothing that I could see.

Nuffles leaped from the nest-box in two bounds and was on my shoulder. "Why do you stand so still watching me?" she asked.

"Tell me what you are at," I whispered.

But I saw the sweet wildness in her eyes and knew that

she would not tell.  So I lingered, hearing the high-pitched
note of two goldcrests in the larch, and all the while
looking out for this unaccountable invisible thing that
was in the wood wherever Nuffles was.  What was she
hiding from me?  Perhaps to-day she packed her trunks for
to-morrow's journey;  yet what luggage had Nuffles
beyond her own tail?

Humbly I offered her a piece of cake, which she took
from my hands with such gentleness that I marvelled at
the control of her paws and her fingers that closed firmly
over this crumb and not over that. · In spite of being a
little wild thing of tantrums and easy wrath, she was
gentle-hearted and courteous.  The mixture of passionate
feeling and tranquillity was the squirrel mixture.  It made
Nuffles and Yump too.

Expecting nothing, yet everything, I watched her
pluck hay from within the nest-box and sit thoughtfully
with a wisp in her mouth.  She seemed uncertain about her
next step, but when Yump landed on the roof of the nest-
box beside her, he forced her decision, and she immediately
bundled the stuff under her chin, pressing it neatly together with her hands, and made off for the oak whose
thick head hid the magpies' nest.  Blackout followed her
by land while Nuffles went the tree-way, and I followed
Blackout.

The trees were whispering and telling tales, but not
one of them told me the answer to my frequent questions;
and Nuffles carried more hay and more hay from the nest-
box to the magpies' old nest until not one strand of hay
remained.  The willow-wren was sighing her plaintive
requests from the bramble bush; and I shut my eyes and
listened to the multiple sighings of the woodland, which
filled the evening air with a strange sadness.  The whole
wood shivered with the sighs of the willow-wren and robin;
and from the obscurity of the trees came other sighs that I
felt but could scarcely hear, as though the insects and
earthworms raised their voices in lament.  The bold happi-

*Fledgeling willow-wrens.*

*"Both were there, and they*

*required no coaxing to come down."*

*"She accepted each pile."*

"I offered her a piece of cake."

ness of the morning had given way to this. Yet, hearing
the mellow evening note of the blackbird I knew all at
once that the ecstasy of morning had but passed into the
ecstasy of evening. The chirrup of the morning was not
lost in this more solemn hour of evening, and I looked to
Nuffles for her to tell me why I was here at all. Nuffles
glanced at me humorously, and afterwards I wondered how
she had time even for that, and it is true that I wonder to
this day.

At first the sorrowful voice of the woodland sent me
back whence I had come, and I thought that either Nuffles
or Yump were about to die, and that they were building a
nest for themselves that would be their death-bed. For
the little animals are reserved to the last; they will not
die in the open but creep bravely away to their holes where
the eyes of the living may not behold them.

When Nuffles had disappeared into the domed nest with
the last morsel of hay, I said to her: "Don't go, Nuffles.
Stay where I can see you."

She did not answer for ten minutes, and when at last

her face appeared in the doorway, her eyes were dancing. "Where's that Yump?" she asked.

He was having his bedtime wash and brush-up in the oak that had housed him for so many weeks, and nothing would move him until he had finished. I stretched up my hands to him. He gave me a look that was full of meaning, skipped on to my arm, descended rapidly to ground and began to stuff his mouth with dry leaves.

"Good boy," I said, and thought how pleasant a thing it was to see two companions working together for the common good. Without asking my leave he made a staircase of me between the ground and the oak. But to my amazement it was not the umbrella-oak he chose, but his old friend. He vaulted two boughs and was in the nest-box with his precious bundle of leaves. Now *where* would they sleep? In the hay-bed of her choice or the leafy bed of his? It was all very confusing to the lay mind. I had been let into a secret; but what is the use of being told such a thing when you are not told what the secret is?

While I was thinking about Yump with my eyes fixed on the pophole-door, Nuffles interrupted abruptly by hopping on to my back. She shattered all my ideas of her by setting her teeth in the cloth of my coat and tugging fiercely at the material. The unexpected onslaught took me by surprise, but through the rush of astonishment I thought: This is the sad secret. Nuffles has a touch of the sun, and Yump's intuition has told him to make up another bed for to-night. . . .

So I placed my hand consolingly on Nuffles' back and tried to stroke her; but she would have none of it. Thumping her hind feet in a paddy, she hurried round to my front, and came up before me, so that I looked in her face. And sunstroke or not, I could not be blind to the question in her eyes. Just as she had often demanded a nut or a bite of toast, so now she flung out her challenge: "Give it to me—*quick!*"

At an utter loss, I said: "What is it you want?" and offered her my last nut.

"Oh, hurry, hurry!" she cried, and she was dancing mad, and began to tear at my collar and the frayed edges of my cuff. I would have given her anything in my power and I was dejected and sad that Nuffles should behave like this while I stood like solid wood without an idea in my head. She would now rob me of my coat; and I took off my coat and threw it on the ground, and Nuffles pounced on it like a crazy thing, biting at material that would not be torn away. She returned to attack me then, clutching at my arm; and her nails went hard into my flesh. She seized my handkerchief, twirled it round and round between her paws into a neat bundle and ran off with it in her mouth. I let it go, and Blackout, having watched her race into the tree and vanish into the magpies' nest, stepped up beside me and said: "A bit over-excited, isn't she?"

Highly strung, I thought, and I looked over to Yump, but there was no sign of him, for he had barricaded himself into the nest-box. Scarcely had Nuffles gone than she was back again; and suddenly I recognised the question in her eyes, and my heart leaped with hope as I thought for a second time: THIS IS THE SECRET.

Hurriedly I searched in all my pockets for a second handkerchief. Finding one, I gave it to her, and she seized it with gratitude, and scampered swiftly up into the magpies' nest. Finding string in one pocket I thrust it at her, and now I hurried with her.

We had a job to be done, a duty to fulfil. We worked together. She took the string, and while she was away I pulled strands from the tattered cuffs of my coat, and put them into neat little bundles all ready for her. She accepted each pile and hastened away to the magpies' nest, and she was never long away, but returned again and again until I seemed to have nothing more to give; but she was less frantic now. Kneeling down, I plucked dry grass from the tufty bits and gathered dry leaves together, working swiftly to plan like one who is in danger and must work quickly before it is too late. She said the grass was fine, but she discarded the leaves because they were blankets fit for bachelors' beds only; and I had not known this, and was glad to remember what she told me.

Toward the end she was not in a bustle any more. She took my offerings with an air of being well satisfied with what she had done; and I could have laughed at the frenzy that had possessed her half an hour ago. Right up to the end I worked with her, and as long as she sought materials I found them for her. When we were finished I fell to wondering what this wild red squirrel would have done if she had been quite alone. If this chance attachment to a human had never come into her life, she would have gone without bits of string and threads from an old coat; she would have used her own natural materials.

The moment came for me to ask: "Is your nest-building over? May I go now?" And looking at the contented expression upon her brown face, I recognised at last the immortality of the squirrels as already I had seen the everlasting lives of the shrews and the mice, the stoats and weasels and foxes, and of the insects, and of the wild birds. So I turned to run home, and Blackout ran her foot-race beside me, casting right and left to test the currents of the air, and raising her glad head into the wind.

We slept that night and returned early in the morning. The woodland babbled and shook with triumphant laughter; the birds made merry in thicket and tree, and the little animals rustled the leaves and rejoiced. I stood beneath the magpies' nest greatly wondering.

"Go closer," said Blackout, sitting under the tree and gazing hard at the ball of sticks.

So I went nearer and put up my hand, and then Nuffles herself came floating through the trees like a flying squirrel and landed on my back. Her face was undisturbed, as though nothing had happened since I left her beyond night passing into day, and I hovered foolishly before the nest, fearful of knowing that I had lost my head yesterday and dreamed. It was the same gnarled tree, the same oven-shaped nest, and the same breeze blowing softly from the south-west. And the same red squirrel. Slowly, with hesitation, I pushed my hand through the uneven doorway of the nest. The warmth of the hay was full of significance. My fingers touched soft material—probably pieces of my own coat. Down into the warm depths of the bedclothes, and I touched a living thing that squeaked once and was silent. I took hold of something smaller than the smallest baby rabbit, yet bigger than the largest baby mouse. It was in my hand and I was looking at it. Pink-skinned, hairless, blind, with exquisite pink baby hands and tiny nails. And a tail. It snuggled into the palm of my hand while Nuffles sat nibbling a chunk of cheese on my shoulder. Feeling again in the nest I withdrew three other pink lumps. Four squirrel babies in the palm of my hand. Quickly I put them back. This then was not the end but the beginning.

I listened to the words of the woodland: the spotted flycatcher feeding her young in the ivy; the whitethroat playing with brown-throated fledglings in the bramble; the willow-wren with her canary-green offspring in the sallow. And the pigeons had laid their twin white eggs in the firs, while the hawks had laid their bold clutches in the tree further on; and down below the furry animals gambolled with litters of young in secret holes beneath the ground. These were perennial and undying. It was June, the month of eternal life. Garrulous June. I need not have quaked with fear for my squirrels. Those two red harum-scarums had never reached the boundary and the conclusion. With the migrant birds and the rustling animals and the cold-footed insects, they were a fragment of the whole.

The animal push of immortality had swung them through the trees of to-morrow. Their triumphant voice would echo down the corridors of the trees for a hundred years.

Blackout stepped with dignity across the clearing. Pausing at the umbrella-oak, she looked up at the nursery just as Nuffles slipped carefully through the door; she walked across to the other oak then and fixed her eyes upon the nest-box which held Yump still sleeping. Then she dropped her head, with her mind made up, and ran quickly to my side. Thrusting her muzzle sharply into my hand to draw my full attention, she looked up at me with gentle authority; and her ears were depressed as they always were when she was asking a grave question.

"What does it all MEAN?" she said.

"Mean?" I said slowly, taken unawares. "Well, just that it's only the end of a chapter, after all, and not the end of the whole book."

Her ears shot up. "Is that why you are so glad?"

"Yes."

Her tail swung earnestly in slow rhythm from side to side.

"Let's celebrate!" Blackout said.